Workbook

New International Edition

Grade 5

Tara Lievesley, Deborah Herridge
Series editor: John Stringer

PEARSON

Pearson Education Limited is a company incorporated in England and Wales having its registered office at Edinburgh Gate, Harlow, Essex, CM20 2JE.

Registered company number: 872828

Text © Pearson Education Limited 2012
First published 2003. This edition published 2012.

www.pearsonglobalschools.com

20 19 18 17 16 15 14 13
IMP 10 9 8 7 6 5 4 3 2

British Library Cataloguing in Publication Data
A catalogue record for this book is available from the British Library

ISBN 978 0 43513 382 5

Edited by Glenys Davis
Designed by Ian Foulis
Original illustrations © Pearson Education Limited, 2003, 2009, 2012
Illustrated by Ian Foulis, Steve Evans and Simon Rumble, Beehive Illustration Ltd
Cover photo: Alamy Images
Printed and bound in Malaysia, CTP-VP

Acknowledgements
The publisher would like to thank the following for their kind permission to reproduce their photographs:

(Key: b-bottom; c-centre; l-left; r-right; t-top)

All other images © Pearson Education

In some instances we have been unable to trace the owners of copyright material, and we would appreciate any information that would enable us to do so.

Contents

WS 1

Microbes and you

Why should you:

1 Cover your mouth when you sneeze?

_____

2 Cover your mouth when you cough?

_____

3 Wash your hands after you go to the toilet?

_____

4 Wash your hands after touching an animal?

_____

Ali was cooking.

> He didn't wash his hands.
> He didn't wipe the surfaces.
> He sneezed a lot.
> His cat kept licking the bowl.
> He pushed his hair back with his hands.
> He went to the toilet and then back to cooking.
> The cooking food smelt good. He ate it before it was ready.

Give three reasons why Ali was ill after this meal.

1 _____

2 _____

3 _____

Class 5J's report

Our challenge – Which conditions grow the most microbes?

What we think – We think that more microbes will grow in warm, damp conditions.

What we did –

- We kept our bread in four different places.
- We put each slice of bread in a different plastic bag.
- We made two slices wet.
- We sealed the bags. We put two in a cold place. We put two in a warm place.
- We counted the colonies after four days.

1 What do you think happened?

_____

2 Why did this happen?

_____

3 Why are these the best conditions for microbes?

_____

What do microbes need to grow well?

Use this table to record the data from your investigation.

Conditions	What grew and why?
warm and damp	
warm and dry	
cold and damp	
cold and dry	

Put your results on this bar chart.

Microbe growth

Number of colonies

25

20

15

10

5

0

Conditions

Investigating microbes

Aisha knew that yeast was a living microbe. She knew that it fed on sugar.

She made four cups of sugary water. She stirred a spoonful of yeast into each one. The water in each pot was at a different temperature. She waited an hour. Then she looked to see what was happening.

This is what she found.

Temperature of the water	What the yeast looked like
ice-cold	no change
cold	some bubbling
warm	lots of bubbles
very hot	nothing

Why did she get these results? What had happened to the yeast:

1 in the ice-cold water?

_____

2 in the cold water?

_____

3 in the warm water?

_____

4 in the very hot water?

_____

5 What are the three conditions yeast needs to grow and reproduce?

a) _____

b) _____

c) _____

Recipe for making bread

Ingredients

225 g strong plain white or plain wholemeal flour
1 level teaspoon salt
1 level teaspoon sugar
15 g (1 level tablespoon) soft margarine
1 sachet dried yeast (6 g)
150 ml warm water – not hot

Equipment

Mixing bowl
Wooden spoon
Measuring jug
Greased baking tray
Wire rack
Cling film brushed with oil

What to do

1 Wash your hands. Collect all the equipment and ingredients together.
2 Put the flour in the mixing bowl and add the sugar and salt.
3 Add the margarine. Rub into the flour using your fingertips.
4 Add the dried yeast. Stir into the flour mix.
5 Add all the water at once to the flour mix. Stir with the wooden spoon.
6 Use your hands when the dough gets difficult to mix. Put the dough on to a floured surface, when it leaves the sides of the bowl clean.
7 The dough will feel tight and bumpy. You must knead it for about 5 minutes, until it feels smooth and stretchy.
8 Shape the dough into your own design. Put it on a greased baking tray.
9 Cover the shape with the cling film. Then put it in a warm place so that the dough will rise.
10 Ask an adult to help you with steps 10–13. Set the oven to 230°C/450°F/ Gas Mark 8.
11 When the loaf shape has doubled in size (after about 30 minutes), remove the cling film. Ask an adult to put the tray in the centre of the oven.
12 Bake the loaf for 20–25 minutes. It will be hot! Ask an adult to take it out with an oven glove. It should be golden brown and sound hollow when tapped underneath.
13 Put the loaf on a wire rack to cool.

Food hygiene

Look at these pictures of an unhygienic kitchen. For each picture explain what is wrong and how the problem can be solved.

Unit 1 assessment

1 Complete the table. Show whether each of these microbes is helpful or harmful.

Microbe	Helpful	Harmful
mould on bread		
bacteria in yoghurt		
yeast in bread		
mould in cheese		
bacteria in compost		
virus for 'flu		

2 Some scientists wanted to see if washing hands prevented the spread of microbes. They tested their theory with bread. They set up the experiment in sealed bags and left it for 5 days. These are their results.

Conditions of bread	Number of colonies
clean hand wiped over surface of bread	5
freshly washed hand wiped over surface of bread	1
dirty hand wiped over surface of bread	10
bread wiped across surface of the floor	15

a) Draw a bar chart of these results on a sheet of paper.

b) How does washing your hands prevent microbes from spreading?

_____

_____

Fruit and vegetables

Use this table to write down the portions of fruit and vegetables you eat this week.

	Fruit	Vegetables
Sunday		
Monday		
Tuesday		
Wednesday		
Thursday		
Friday		
Saturday		

Think about how you could increase your intake of fruit and vegetables.

Name: _____ Date: _____

Heart structure

Use each word once to complete the diagram.

atrium   body   lungs   ventricle   lungs   body

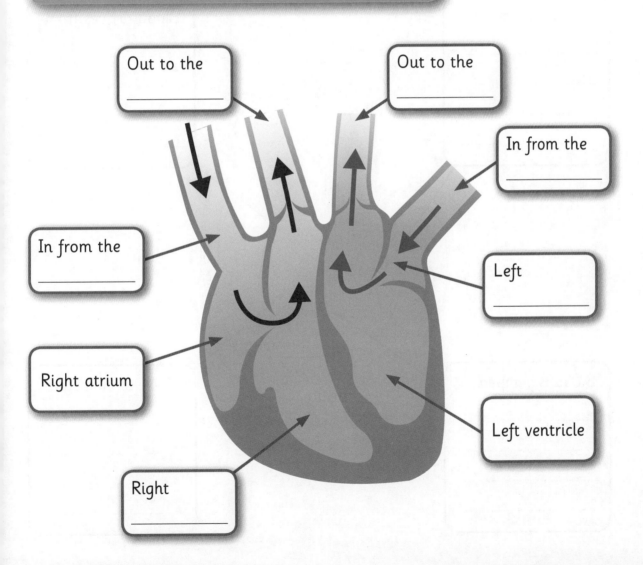

Out to the
_____

Out to the
_____

In from the
_____

In from the
_____

Left
_____

Right atrium

Left ventricle

Right
_____

How the blood moves around the body

Label the different parts of the heart. Draw arrows to show the direction of blood flow.

Write some notes in the boxes to explain what is happening.

Blood arrives from
_____
_____
_____
_____

Blood arrives from
_____
_____
_____
_____

lungs

body

Blood is pumped to
_____
_____
_____
_____

Blood is pumped to
_____
_____
_____
_____

How many pulses?

Mark all the places you can feel your heart beating on this body outline. Label these pulse points.

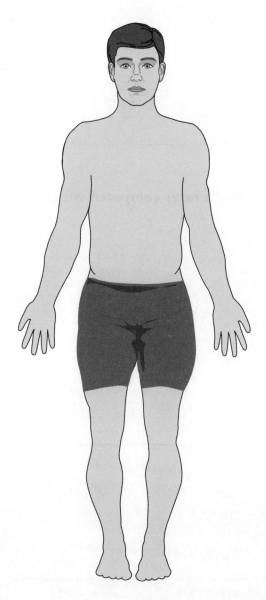

People's heart rates

Use this table to record the heart rates of different members of your family.
Draw a line graph to show your results.

Person	Age	Heart rate at rest

Heart rates compared with age

Heart rate
(beats per minute)

Age (years)

What does your graph suggest?

_____

_____

Exercising your heart

Use this table to record the results from your investigation.

Type of exercise	Pulse rate 1	Pulse rate 2	Pulse rate 3	Average pulse rate

Which exercise increases your heart rate most? Why do you think that is?

_____

_____

Try doing the same exercise for different lengths of time. What should you do between each exercise session? Why?

_____

_____

What happens when you exercise for at least an hour? Why do you think this is?

_____

_____

WS 14 What is your pulse rate?

Use Class 5E's results to make a bar chart below.

Type of exercise	Pulse rate (bpm)
sitting	70
jogging	95
running	130
sit-ups	105
skipping	124

Heart rates after exercise

Type of exercise

What does your chart show?

_____

_____

Dr Quitit's notes

Dr Quitit's notes are incomplete. Fill the gaps by doing research on smoking.

● Every year _____ people die from lung cancer caused by smoking.

● Smoking causes _____ deaths from bronchitis each year.

● The number of deaths from heart disease caused by smoking in my country each year is _____ .

● Today, about _____ % of men and _____ % of women smoke.

● List three reasons why we shouldn't smoke.

_____

_____

_____

_____

_____

_____

The effects of drugs

Complete the sentences:

1 A drug causes our bodies to _____ .

2 A drug can make your heart _____ faster.

3 A drug can _____ your thinking.

4 A drug can make you _____ to react.

5 It is hard to _____ using an addictive drug.

Which of these are drugs? Circle them.

Coffee

Bread

Tea

Cigarettes

Butter

Soft drink

Unit 2 assessment 1

1 Where in your body is your heart? _____

2 Describe two changes you notice about your body when you exercise.

_____

3 The graph shows how heartbeat changes when you exercise. Use it to answer the questions below.

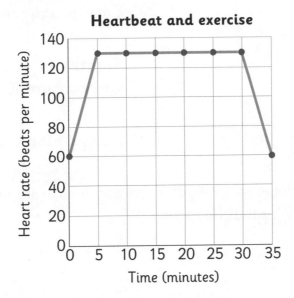

a) What was your heart rate before you started running?

_____ beats per minute

b) What happened to your heart rate in the first five minutes that you were running?

_____

c) How long did you run for? How do you know?

_____

Unit 2 assessment 2

4 Why does smoking make a football player less fit?

_____

_____

_____

5 Match up the body part and its function.

Heart   Carries oxygen around the body

Blood   Breathe in air, exchange oxygen
                               and carbon dioxide

Lungs

                               Pumps blood around the body

6 The hearts of athletes return to their resting heart rate very quickly after exercise. Explain why that happens.

_____

_____

_____

The life of a plant

What order should the pictures go in? Number them 1–6. Use the words below. Label each stage in the plant's life cycle. Which two stages/pictures are missing?

> **Pollination   Fertilization   Seed dispersal   Flower dies**
> **Germination   Growth   Flowering   Seed formation**

_____

_____

_____

_____

_____

_____

Name: _____ **Date:** _____

WS 20 Plant life cycles

Draw a plant life cycle. Show the stages between the seed and the fully grown plant. Show the stages between the fully grown plant and the seed. Use these words to label your life cycle drawing.

> Fertilized ovum   Fruit   Germination   Seedling
> Adult plant   Seeds on the ground

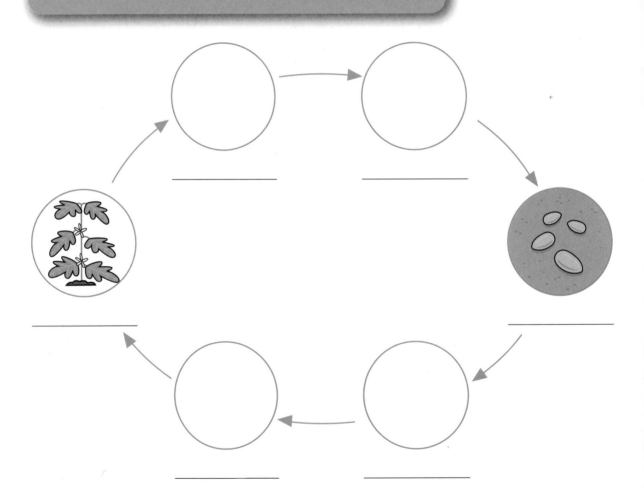

Seed dispersal

Plants use many methods to disperse their seeds. Put these plants into the correct boxes below. Then try to add three more plants that you know to each box.

> **Banana tree** **Grass** **Apple tree** **Coconut palm** **Orange tree**
> **Water Lily** **Sycamore tree** **Mangrove** **Pandorea**

Seeds dispersed by animals eating the fruit	Seeds dispersed by water	Seeds dispersed by the wind
e.g. Date palm	e.g. Sea bean	e.g. Grass

Spinners

Make spinners like these to test. Check that they are the same shape and style. Only the size of the wings should change!

Place a paper-clip on the spinner to act as the seed.

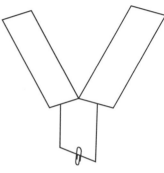

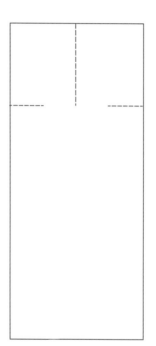

Flying spinners

Use the tables to record the results from your investigation. Make a prediction first.

Order to fall	Predicted	Actual
1st		
2nd		
3rd		
4th		
5th		
6th		

Length of wing (cm)	Time to fall 2 m (in seconds)

Which spinner fell fastest?

_____

What do you notice about the pattern of your results?

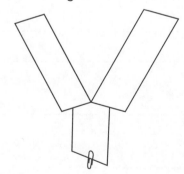

WS 24

Which spinner falls fastest?

Our challenge – How does changing the length of the wing affect the time it takes for the spinner to fall?

What we think – We think that a spinner with longer wings will take longer to fall. If it takes longer to fall it can travel further in the air.

What we did –

- We measured the length of the spinner's wing.
- We dropped it from 2 m and started the stopwatch.
- We recorded the time.
- We changed the wing length and dropped it again from the same height.
- We repeated this for five different lengths of wing.

How we made it fair – We kept the shape of the wing and the height we dropped it from the same.

Results –

Length of wing (cm)	Time to fall 2 m (in seconds)
10	4.8
5	8.0
8	6.1
12	3.2
16	2.5

1 Which spinner took the longest time to fall? _____

2 Which spinner took the shortest time to fall? _____

3 The smaller the spinner the faster it spun.
Why did this make a difference? _____

4 The very big wings folded.
Why did this make a difference? _____

WS 25 How many seedlings did you grow?

Use this table to record the data from your investigation. Then complete the bar chart below.

Conditions	Number of seeds germinated

Seed germination

How did you make your investigation fair? _____

_____

How long does it take?

Look at the graph and answer the questions. A gestation period is the time a pregnancy lasts – the time the baby is inside the mother.

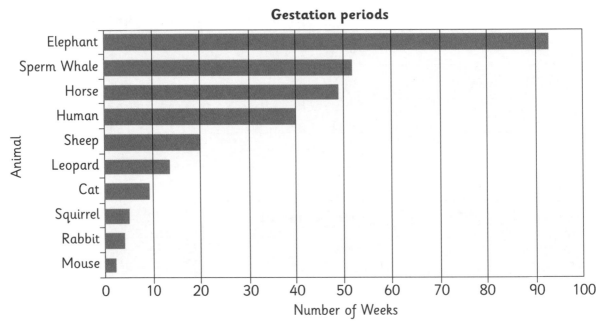

Gestation periods

1 What is the gestation period for: a) a sheep? _____

b) a horse? _____

2 What is the difference in weeks between the gestation time of a leopard and a human?

_____

3 What pattern links the gestation times of these mammals and their adult size?

_____

4 Human gestation is very long for our adult body size. Why do you think that is? _____

_____

Family trees

Look at this family tree. Use it to answer the questions.

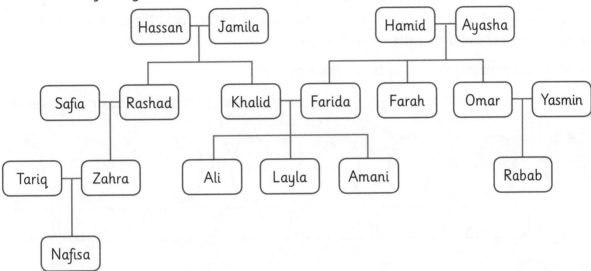

1 What are Layla's parents called?

_____

2 Who is Farida's brother? What is his relationship to Ali?

_____

3 How many grandchildren does Hassan have?

_____

4 What are the names of Rabab's aunts?

_____

5 Write the names of all the grandparents in the family tree.

_____

6 How many cousins does Zahra have?

_____

WS 28 Your family tree

Use this chart to draw your own family tree.

Draw and name yourself and any brothers and sisters you have on the bottom line. You may need to add more boxes!

Draw and name your parents on the next line.

See if you can get back to your grandparents, and perhaps great-grandparents.

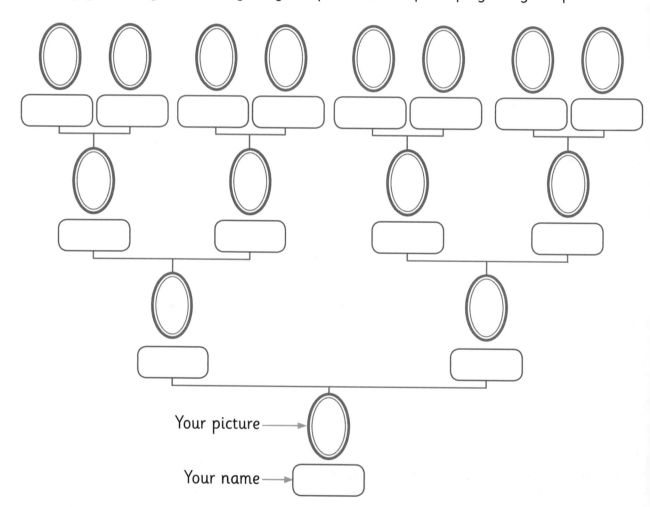

Your picture ⟶

Your name ⟶

Unit 3 assessment 1

1 Some flowering plants are wind pollinated. What does this mean?

_____

_____

2 What ways are seeds dispersed? _____

_____

3 The children in Class 5 found some information about birds' eggs.

Bird Egg	Robin	Blackbird	Crow	Raven
Size (mm)	20 x 16	29 x 21	43 x 30	50 x 33
Time to hatch (days)	13	14	19	20

What is the pattern linking the size of these eggs and the time taken to hatch?

_____

4 Tariq found an egg 60 mm long. How long might it take to hatch?

_____

5 Jamila found an egg 35 mm long. How long might it take to hatch?

_____

WS 30

Unit 3 assessment 2

6 These stages in the life cycle of a flowering plant are not in the right order.

A	Growing plant
B	Pollination
C	Dispersal of seed
D	Germination
E	Flower production

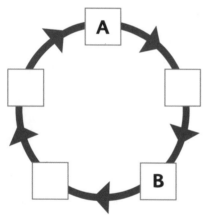

Fill in the letters in the correct order to show a plant's complete life cycle.

7 Many adult animals die soon after reproducing. Humans do not. Explain why.

_____

_____

_____

8 Name some ways that the life cycles of plants and animals are alike.

_____

_____

_____

Light sources

Nadima is going into a deep, dark cellar. She wants to find a lost toy. There is no light. What should she take to find her toy? Which of these would help?

1 Tick (✓) any that are sources of light.

- An electric torch or flashlight
- A shiny mirror
- A candle
- Her shiny bike reflector

2 Explain two of your choices.

I know that a _____ is a light source because

_____

I know that a _____ is not a light source because

_____

3 The Moon is not a source of light. It reflects light. We can still see the Moon on dark nights. Why is this?

Even though it is _____ time, the _____ is still shining.

Even though we can't see the _____ it is still

_____ .

The light from the _____ is reflected from the

_____ .

Which material casts the darkest shadow?

Use this table. Record the data from your investigation.

material	shade of shadow
thick cardboard	dark/light/no shadow
cork tile	dark/light/no shadow
fur fabric	dark/light/no shadow
foil	dark/light/no shadow
writing paper	dark/light/no shadow
tissue paper	dark/light/no shadow
plastic sheet	dark/light/no shadow
cling film	dark/light/no shadow
greaseproof paper	dark/light/no shadow

1 Which material has the darkest shadow? Why?

_____

2 Which materials cast no shadows? Why?

_____

3 What shadow will a sheet of drawing paper cast? Why?

_____

How do the shadows change?

WS 33

Use this table to record the data from your investigation.

Distance from light (cm)	Height of shadow (cm)

Complete this line graph to show your results clearly:

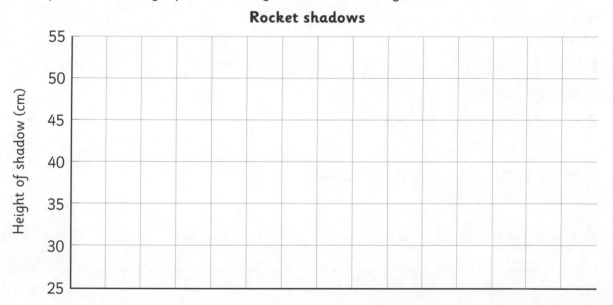

Rocket shadows

Height of shadow (cm)

55
50
45
40
35
30
25

Distance from light (cm)

WS 34

Mission to Mars

We performed a shadow puppet play. It showed a rocket travelling to Mars. It is a very simple special effect. This is how we did it.

To show the rocket launching, we used a puppet on a stick. We held it between a light source and a white card screen. We measured the distance between the puppet and the light, and the size of the shadow on the screen. Then we moved the puppet to see what happened.

Our results are in the table.

So can you guess what we did now? We started with our rocket puppet very close to the light source behind the screen and gradually moved it further away. This makes it look like it was getting smaller and moving towards Mars!

Distance from light (cm)	Height of shadow (cm)
6	53
8	46
10	39
20	33
30	31
40	30
50	29
60	28
70	27
80	27
90	27
100	26

1 How far from the light was the biggest rocket? _____ cm

2 How far from the light was the smallest rocket? _____ cm

3 When is the rocket half its full size?

_____ cm

4 Write a general rule. The further the from the light, the _____

_____ .

How do shadows change shape throughout the day?

Use this table to record the data from your investigation.

Time of day	Length of shadow (cm)

Complete this line graph to show your results clearly:

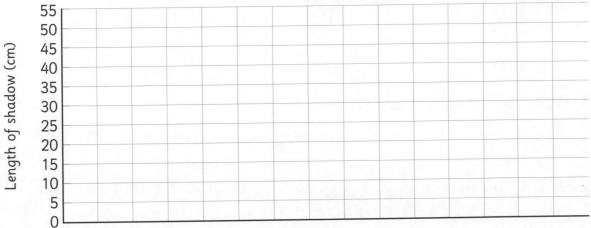

Shadows throught the day

WS 36

Class 5's report

Our challenge – How do shadows change shape through the day?

What we think – The shape and size of a shadow will change as the Sun appears to move across the sky.

What we did –

- We put a stick in a bottle in the playground.
- We measured the length of its shadow every hour.

How we made it fair – We put the stick in the middle of the playground. It was always in the Sun.

Results –

Time of day	Length of shadow (cm)
9.00	19
10.00	9
11.00	1
12.00	9
1.00	18
2.00	33
3.00	55

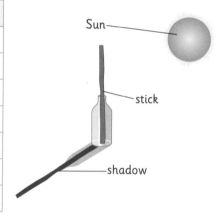

1 What did Class 5 find out?

_____

_____

2 How did the shadow shape change?

_____

3 What do you think happened to the direction of the shadow?

_____

Investigating shadows

Here is a record of changing shadows through the day.

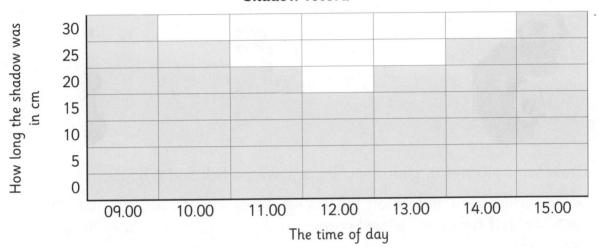

Shadow record

Answer these questions:

1 How long was the shadow at noon? _____ cm.

2 At what time was the shadow longest?

At _____ and _____ .

3 Did the shadow get longer or shorter through the morning?

_____

4 Did the shadow get longer or shorter through the afternoon?

_____

5 The shadow length changed. But the shadow will change in another way, too. How?

_____

Can you believe your eyes?

Some shapes are exactly the same on both sides if you cut them in half. These shapes are called symmetrical. Use a small mirror to complete these pictures.

Draw some pictures of your own. Try a flower, a bell and a house.

Some mirrors bend and distort reflections. Cover a card tube with foil. Put the tube, which is now a cylindrical mirror, on the circles below. What happens to the lines?

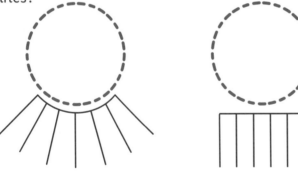

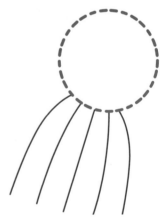

Which way will the clown face?

WS 39

Seeing things

Diya is watching TV. Draw an arrow to show how she can see the TV.

When light hits a smooth shiny surface it is reflected from it at an angle. The angle of reflection is the same as the angle of the light coming to the mirror. It is in the opposite direction, like this:

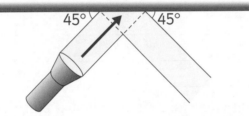

Use a ruler and a protractor to draw the path of the reflected light from the torch in these pictures. Write in the angle that the light enters and leaves the mirror.

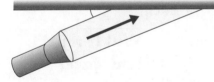

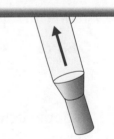

Now try drawing two of your own.

 **WS 40**

Testing reflective materials

1 Look at this table. Answer the questions in the table. Put 'yes' or 'no' for each material.

One has been done for you.

Object	Does it reflect light?	Will it reflect a torch or flashlight beam?	Will it reflect your face?
mirror	Yes	Yes	Yes
wooden chair			
cola can			
glass bottle			
water in a bowl			

2 Jamal had a roll of kitchen foil. He unrolled a piece carefully. Then he screwed it up. Finally, he smoothed it out again as much as he could. It was still crumpled.

Answer the questions in the table. Put 'yes' or 'no' for each.

Object	Does it reflect light?	Will it reflect a torch or flashlight beam?	Will it reflect your face?
smooth kitchen foil			
screwed up kitchen foil			
crumpled kitchen foil			

WS 41

Unit 4 assessment 1

1 Some materials let light through but some do not. Draw a line from these materials to their correct group.

wood   transparent   frosted glass

glass   translucent   cardboard

tissue paper   opaque   cling film

2 Ziad has drawn his shadow.

a) Explain what Ziad has done wrong and what he should have drawn.

_____

_____

b) Mark an 'X' where you think the Sun is in Ziad's picture.

c) Explain how Ziad's shadow was made. _____

_____

3 Look at this shadow. It was made at 9 a.m. Draw the shadow you would expect to see at midday on the picture. Explain why it has changed.

_____

_____

_____

_____

Unit 4 assessment 2

4 Sian shone a light at the wall. Then she put her hand in the light beam. She could see its shadow on the wall. Which two ways could she make the shadow larger? Tick (✓) them.

- Move her hand nearer the wall.

- Move her hand closer to the torch.

- Move the torch further from her hand.

- Move the torch closer to her hand.

5 Anil noticed that his shadow, cast by the Sun, was different in the middle of the day from his shadow in the early morning. How had it changed?

_____

_____

_____

6 'The Sun moves across the sky,' said Anna's little brother. 'It seems to,' said Anna, 'but really . . .'

Explain why the Sun appears to move. Draw a picture to help.

WS 43

Puddle puzzle

A water drop in a puddle is trapped like a prisoner. It can escape, but only through evaporation from the surface of the puddle.

Measure the width of a puddle in the playground every 30 minutes. Record your results in this table.

Look at the pattern of your results. What do you notice? _____

Time (minutes)	Width (cm)
0	
30	
60	
90	
120	

_____

Why might the number of water 'prisoners' escaping slow down? (Think about the size of the puddle's surface!) _____

_____

Draw a graph of your results. Label the axes. Will it be a bar chart or a line graph? _____

My shrinking puddle

How does a container's shape change the speed of evaporation?

Use this table to record the data from your investigation.

Container	Diameter of container (cm)	Volume of water at the beginning (a) (cm³)	Volume of water after one week (b) (cm³)	Volume of water that evaporated (a–b) (cm³)

What did you find out? If you draw a bar chart or line graph, explain what it shows.

_____

_____

_____

_____

_____

_____

WS 45

Ajay's report

My challenge – To find out how container shape effects evaporation.

What I think – Water will evaporate faster from a wider container.

What I did –

- I poured 500 cm³ of water into each of five different-shaped containers.
- I placed the containers on the windowsill and measured their diameter.
- I measured how much water was left in the container after one week.
- I worked out how much water had evaporated from each container.

Results –

Container	Diameter of container (cm)	Volume of water at the beginning (cm³) (a)	Volume of water after one week (cm³) (b)	Volume of water that evaporated (cm³) (a–b)
bowl	20	500	450	50
pot	15	500	400	100
tall jar	10	500	480	20
thin vase	5	500	490	10
tray	30	500	350	150

What I found out – The tray allowed the greatest evaporation. It has the largest diameter. More water can get away because more water is in contact with the air.

Has Ajay drawn the correct conclusion from his results?

_____

What could Ajay have done differently? How did he make this a fair test?

_____

Speedy evaporation

Prediction – Write down the place where you think washing will dry fastest.

_____

_____

Use this table to record the data from your investigation.

Where I put the washing	How wet at the start	How wet in the morning	How wet in the afternoon	How wet in the evening

Answer these questions:

1 Why did you make your prediction?

_____

_____

2 What made the washing dry fastest?

_____

_____

Amani's report

My challenge – To find out the best place for drying washing.

What I think – I think that the washing placed in the airing cupboard will dry the quickest.

What I did –

- I poured water over four identical pieces of cloth.
- I hung the cloths in different places around the house.
- I left them out all day.
- I felt how dry they were on three different occasions.

How I made it fair – The cloths were the same size and material. Each cloth had the same amount of water poured over it. I made sure that none of the places were in a draught.

Results –

Where I put the washing	How wet at the start	How wet in the morning	How wet in the afternoon	How wet in the evening
window	soaking	dripping	wet	damp
fridge	soaking	dripping	wet and cold	wet and cold
warm kitchen	soaking	wet	damp	dry
outside	soaking	wet	dry	dry

What I found out – The best place to dry cloths was outside.

Amani has not given reasons for outside being the best drying place. What are the reasons? _____

_____

_____

Water in the desert

This is a cross-section through a hole in the desert. Some explorers have made a water-collector. Explain how it works. Write your answers in the boxes.

1 _____
_____
_____
_____
_____

2 _____
_____
_____
_____
_____

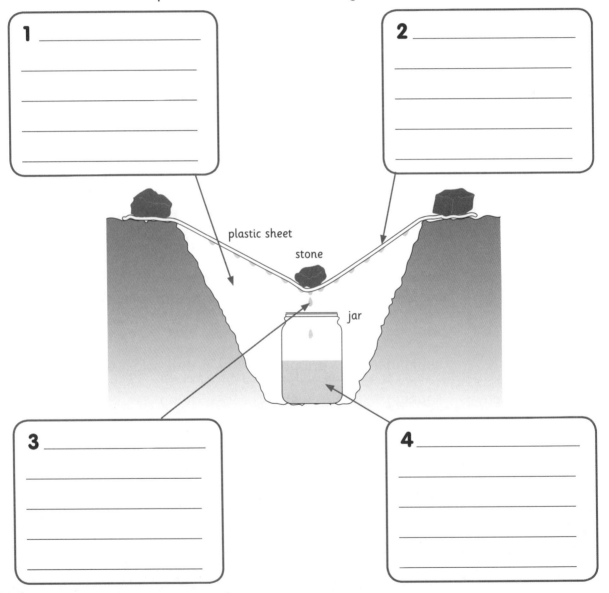

plastic sheet

stone

jar

3 _____
_____
_____
_____

4 _____
_____
_____
_____

WS 49 Evaporation and condensation

Select words from the box and insert them in the right place to complete the diagram.

solidifying evaporating liquid freezing condensing
melting solid heat boiling cool gas

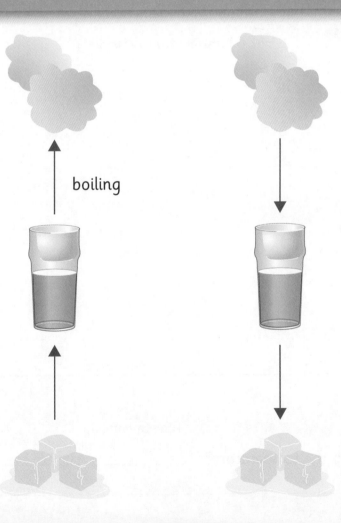

boiling

WS 50 Changes in water temperature over time

Use this table to record the data from your investigation.

Time (minutes)									
Temperature (°C)									

Complete this line graph to show your results clearly:

Temperature record

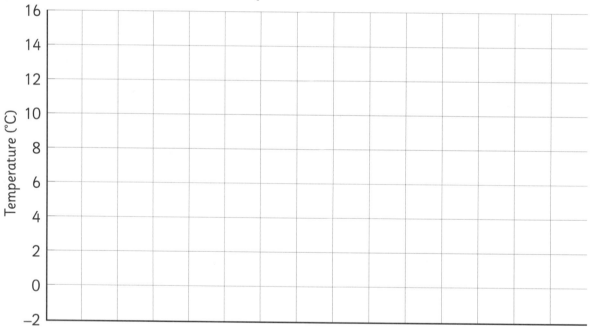

Time (minutes)

What happens to the temperature? _____

_____

Melting ice

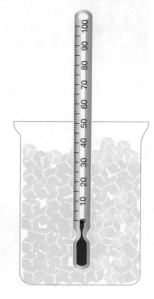

Our challenge – At what temperature does ice melt?

What we think – We think that the ice will melt at 0°C.

What we did –

- We put crushed ice into a container.
- We used a thermometer to take temperature every minute.
- We looked to see what the temperature was when the ice became water.

Results –

Time (minutes)	0	1	2	3	4	5	6	7	8	9	10
Temperature (°C)	–2	–2	–1	0	0	2	4	7	10	13	16

What we found out – The ice became water at close to 0°C. This is the freezing point of water. The temperature kept going up.

Answer these questions:

1 When will the temperature stop going up?

_____

2 What could you have done differently?

_____

_____

3 How might the results have been affected?

_____

_____

Ice balloon

This is how to make and test an ice balloon.

Explain what is happening by writing in the boxes.

1

_____
_____
_____

2

_____
_____
_____

3

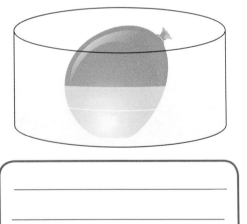

_____
_____
_____

4

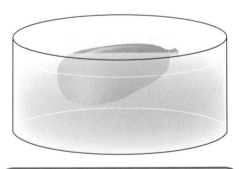

_____
_____
_____

WS 53

The water cycle

Put arrows on this diagram to explain the water cycle, like the blue one between the clouds.

Write what is happening at each stage in the boxes.

5 _____
_____
_____
_____
_____

4 _____
_____
_____
_____
_____

3 _____
_____
_____
_____
_____

2 _____
_____
_____
_____
_____

1 _____
_____
_____
_____
_____

Unit 5 assessment 1

1 Parminder and Jasminder are investigating evaporation. They put the same amount of water in different-shaped dishes in different places round the house.

a) Why is this not a fair test?

_____

_____

b) What should they do to make it a fair test?

_____

_____

c) How should the girls decide where most evaporation has taken place?

_____

_____

d) Explain what evaporation is.

_____

_____

2 Khaled was puzzled. If all the things in the bathroom are the same temperature, why does water condense on the window and mirror? Tick (✓) the right answer.

a) Water is attracted to glass.

b) Glass conducts heat easily, and water vapour reaching it is cooled very quickly.

c) Water condenses everywhere, but you see it best on mirrors and windows.

Unit 5 assessment 2

3 The rain cycle is jumbled. Match each sentence to a number to put it in the right order.

Water evaporates from the surface of the sea. ⎯⎯⎯⎯⎯⎯⎯ | 1 |

Water falls as rain. | 2 |

Water in the clouds condenses. | 3 |

Water rises to form clouds. | 4 |

Water flows in streams and rivers to the sea. | 5 |

4 Explain how evaporation can make liquids pure.

_____

_____

_____

5 Safia's mother put a lid on the pasta she was cooking in a saucepan. 'Even if I forget it, it will stay moist,' she said. How did she know?

_____

_____

_____

6 Salim pegged out his washing on a cloudy morning but it was still wet at midday. In the afternoon the wind blew and the Sun came out. It dried quickly. Explain why this happened.

_____

_____

_____

WS 56 Our solar system

We don't know how many planets there are in the universe. There may be planets round other suns in the universe. Every star could have its own solar system. But we do know about our own Sun, about our own Earth, and its one Moon.

1 Use these numbers to complete the table below.

> 12756 km   3476 km   40076 km   1392000 km   10915 km

	Circumference – the distance all the way round	Diameter – the distance across the middle
Sun	4370880 km	
Earth		
Moon		

2 We know that the Earth is not flat. Here is the evidence. Use these words to complete the sentences.

> shadow   planets   mast   sphere   travel

- You can _____ round the world.
- When a ship appears over the horizon, you see its _____ first, and the body of the ship last of all.
- When there is an eclipse of the Moon, the curved _____ of the Earth crosses the Moon's face.
- Pictures from space show that the Earth is a _____, the shape of a ball.
- The Earth is one of eight spherical _____ in our solar system.

Shoe box space

Make this tennis ball model of the Moon in space.

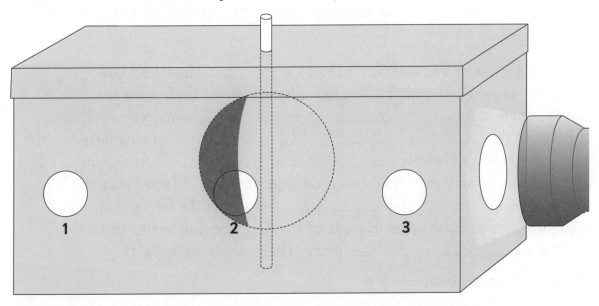

1   2   3

Switch on the torch, look through each of the holes 1, 2 and 3.

What do you notice?

_____

_____

Why does the Moon look different through each hole?

_____

_____

How does the Moon appear to change through a month?

_____

_____

WS 58

Email to penfriend

Complete this email to your penfriend who lives on the other side of the world. Fill in the missing words. Use the words in the box at the bottom of the page.

Dear _____

I wanted to phone you last Saturday afternoon, but Mum said you would be sleeping. I didn't believe her. She explained that when it is daytime here it is _____ where you are. This is because the _____ spins on its axis once every 24 hours. When the _____ is shining on one side of the Earth, the other side is in darkness. I found that the Sun stays _____ and it is the Earth that is spinning. As the Earth spins in front of the Sun, the Sun seems to be in a _____ place. That's amazing, isn't it?

Please write back soon.

Love _____ .

| Sun   Earth   night-time   still   different |

WS 59

Our turning Earth

1 How many times does the Earth spin on its axis each day?

| 1 | 7 | 28 | 365 |

2 How many times does the Earth spin on its axis each year?

| 1 | 7 | 28 | 365 |

3 How many days does the Earth take to circle or orbit the Sun?

| 1 | 7 | 28 | 365 |

4 How many days does it take for the Moon to orbit the Earth?

| 1 | 7 | 28 | 365 |

5 Draw the Sun and the Earth as two circles.

On your drawing, draw arrows to show:
- which is spinning
- which way it is spinning
- which is orbiting
- which way it is orbiting.

Movement of the Earth

Look at the diagrams of the Sun and the Earth.

1 Shade the part of the Earth where it is night.

2 Look at the places marked X. Is it day or night there?

3 On these diagrams mark a place that is day and a place that is night.

Day   Night

Moon diary

Each night, draw the shape of the Moon as you see it in one of the circles below.

1 ◯	2 ◯	3 ◯	4 ◯
5 ◯	6 ◯	7 ◯	8 ◯
9 ◯	10 ◯	11 ◯	12 ◯
13 ◯	14 ◯	15 ◯	16 ◯
17 ◯	18 ◯	19 ◯	20 ◯
21 ◯	22 ◯	23 ◯	24 ◯
25 ◯	26 ◯	27 ◯	28 ◯

What pattern do you notice? _____

_____

_____

WS 62 The Moon

What do you know about the Moon?
Which of these statements are true? Circle '**True**' or '**False**'.

1 The Moon changes shape as the Earth's shadow crosses it.　**True / False**

2 The Moon changes shape because clouds cover part of it.　**True / False**

3 The Moon changes shape because it orbits the Earth.　**True / False**

4 The Moon changes shape because of the shadow of the Sun's light on it.　**True / False**

5 The Moon changes shapes because planets cast a shadow on it.　**True / False**

6 The Moon orbits the Earth.　**True / False**

7 The Moon orbits the Sun.　**True / False**

8 The Moon reflects the light of the Sun.　**True / False**

9 The Moon shines with its own light.　**True / False**

10 The Moon takes about 28 days to orbit the Earth.　**True / False**

Our tilting Earth

The Earth is tilted at 23° as it orbits the Sun.
Sometimes our part of the Earth is tilted towards the Sun.

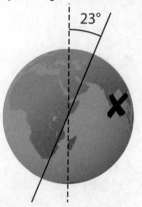

Sometimes it is tilted away from the Sun.

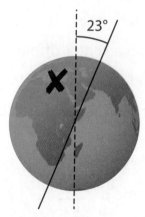

Explain how this makes it hotter where you live.

_____

_____

_____

_____

How the Earth travels

Nicolaus Copernicus lived six hundred years ago. He was born in Poland. People believed that the Earth was the centre of the universe. But Copernicus first said that the planets orbit the Sun.

Galileo Galilei was an Italian scientist. He studied space with a telescope. He first saw moons round another planet. He saw three of the four moons of Jupiter.

Galileo used his observations to prove that Copernicus was right. Galileo proved that the Earth orbits the Sun.

Complete these sentences:

1 The Sun is at the centre of our _____ system.

2 The Earth, and all the other _____ , orbit the Sun.

3 They travel round it in huge ellipses. An ellipse is a flattened

_____ .

4 The Earth takes around _____ days to orbit the Sun.

5 We call this time a _____ .

6 Every 365 days, the Earth completes an _____ .

7 As it orbits, the Earth is also _____ round.

The seasons

The Earth travels round the Sun once a year. The Earth moves at an angle.
So at some times of the year, the Sun shines directly on your home.
At other times, it shines at an angle.

These differences give us the seasons.

1 Use a big ball for the Earth.
Use a torch for the Sun.
Stick something small on the ball where you live. That's you!
The Earth turns anticlockwise, looking from above.

2 Model the summer Sun directly overhead. Shine the torch straight down on the place where you live.

3 Model the winter Sun. Shine the torch at an angle on the place where you live.

Now answer these questions:

1 What do you notice about the summer Sun?

a) How big is the area it covers? _____

b) How strong is the light? _____

2 What do you notice about the winter Sun?

a) How big is the area it covers? _____

b) How strong is the light? _____

3 Explain why the Sun is hotter and brighter in the summer than in the winter.

_____

_____

4 If you stand in the Sun, the top of your head and ears, your shoulders and the tops of your feet may burn. Explain why.

_____

WS 66

Unit 6 assessment 1

1 Safia is making a model. Tick (✓) the three best objects she could use to represent the Earth, Sun and Moon.

cushion ☐   tissue box ☐   football ☐

ping-pong ball ☐   tennis ball ☐   beach ball ☐

rugby ball ☐   poppy seed ☐   roll of tape ☐

small coin ☐

2 How many times does the Earth spin on its axis each day?
Circle the correct answer.

1   7   24   28   365

3 Write true or false after each of these sentences.

a) The Earth orbits the Sun. _____

b) The Moon orbits the Earth. _____

c) The Sun orbits the Earth. _____

d) The planets orbit the Earth. _____

4 a) Use the names Sun, Moon and Earth to label the diagram.

C _____

B _____

A _____

b) How long does it take A to orbit C? _____

c) How long does it take B to orbit A? _____

Unit 6 assessment 2

5 Here are two pictures showing the shadow of a tree at different times of the day.

Explain why the shadow has changed.

_____

_____

_____

_____

6 a) Look at this diagram. Shade the part of the Earth where it is night.

b) Is it day or night in Australia? _____

c) Mark a cross on the Earth where it is midday.